G000292804

Help with Homework

Adding and Subtracting

In Year Two (age 7+) your child is expected to be able to:

• Solve problems using addition and subtraction using concrete objects and pictures, including sums involving numbers, quantities and measures.

• Apply their increasing knowledge of mental and written methods to solve addition and subtraction problems.

• Recall and use addition and subtraction facts to 10 fluently, and be able to use related facts up to 100.

• Show that addition of two numbers can be done in any order but that subtraction of one number from another number cannot be done in any order.

• Recognise the inverse relationship between addition and subtraction and use this to check calculations and solve missing number problems (for example $4 + ? = 6$).

Designed by Plum5
Illustrations by Sue King, Sharon Smart and Andy Geeson
Educational consultant Josh Levenson and Nina Filipek

www.autumnchildrensbooks.co.uk

Number bonds to 10

Do you know your numbers bonds to 10?
Write the missing numbers in the boxes.

$$7 + \boxed{} = 10$$

$$8 + \boxed{} = 10$$

$$9 + \boxed{} = 10$$

$$4 + \boxed{} = 10$$

$$5 + \boxed{} = 10$$

☐ + 3 = 10

☐ + 6 = 10

☐ + 1 = 10

☐ + 5 = 10

2 + ☐ = 10

Addition on the farm

Complete these farmyard sums by writing the missing numbers in the boxes.

$\boxed{} + 7 = 12$ $\qquad$ $\boxed{} + 4 = 8$

$7 + \boxed{} = 14$ $\qquad$ $4 + 3 = \boxed{}$

$\boxed{} + 10 = 20$ $\qquad$ $\boxed{} + 9 = 10$

2 + ☐ = 4   7 + 9 = ☐

☐ + 7 = 19   ☐ + 11 = 11

8 + ☐ = 21   18 + 12 = ☐

☐ + 7 = 15   ☐ + 8 = 17

Alien addition

Solve these space sums. Write the answers in the boxes.

15 + 3 = ☐

16 + 2 = ☐

11 + 3 = ☐

18 + 7 = ☐

15 + 9 = ☐

13 + 4 = ☐

26 + 7 = ☐

23 + 9 = ☐

18 + 5 = ☐

91 + 8 = ☐

48 + 3 = ☐

35 + 6 = ☐

67 + 7 = ☐

55 + 6 = ☐

Missing numbers

The answers to these sums are missing. Write in the answers to complete the sums using the numbers in the balloons.

34 + 6 =

83 + 7 =

77 + 3 =

78 + 4 =

53 + 9 =

23 + 6 =

45 + 7 =

88 + 5 =

13 + 9 =

22

82

90

29

62

52

93

40

80

Adding 10s

Work out these sums (they will help you in the next task!).

5 + 8 = ☐   6 + 3 = ☐

2 + 6 = ☐   5 + 1 = ☐

7 + 5 = ☐   8 + 3 = ☐

Now use the sums above to help you answer the questions below.
Hint: 4 + 3 = 7 so **40 + 30 = 70**.
What do you notice about the answers?

50 + 80 = ☐   60 + 30 = ☐

20 + 60 = ☐   50 + 10 = ☐

70 + 50 = ☐   80 + 30 = ☐

Adding 100s

Work out these sums using what you learnt on the previous page.
Hint: 5 + 4 = 9 so **50 + 40 = 90** that means **500 + 400 = 900**!

300 + 200 = ☐   **Hint: 3 + 2 = 5**

400 + 300 = ☐

200 + 700 = ☐

100 + 700 = ☐

200 + 500 = ☐

400 + 500 = ☐

Match the answers

Draw lines to join the sums on the boats to the answers on the anchors.

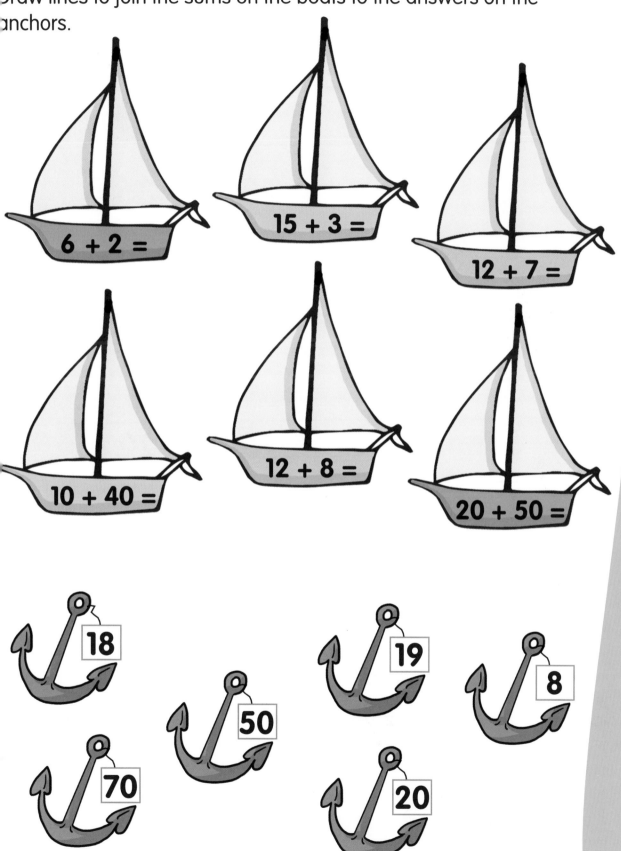

6 + 2 =

15 + 3 =

12 + 7 =

10 + 40 =

12 + 8 =

20 + 50 =

18

50

19

8

70

20

Double digits

Add the two digit numbers together and write your answers in the boxes. If you need to, use a spare piece of paper to work them out.

35 + 22 = ☐

43 + 36 = ☐

25 + 42 = ☐

65 + 24 = ☐

52 + 34 = ☐

76 + 22 = ☐

23 + 51 = ☐

43 + 17 = ☐

67 + 28 = ☐

37 + 51 = ☐

t all adds up

Add the three digit numbers to the two digit numbers and write your answers in the boxes.

178 + 45 =

259 + 52 =

444 + 63 =

153 + 70 =

456 + 16 =

322 + 26 =

244 + 55 =

101 + 23 =

Addition test

Now take the addition test. Do the sums and write the answers in the boxes.

11 + 2 =

6 + 7 =

10 + 5 =

3 + 12 =

A boy has **5** sweets and a girl has **7** sweets. How many sweets do they have altogether?

21 + 6 =

20 + 8 =

17 + 7 =

12 + 6 =

One alien has **8** eyes and another alien has **9** eyes. How many eyes do they have altogether?

13 + 12 = ☐   20 + 16 = ☐

34 + 23 = ☐   42 + 16 = ☐

48 + 31 = ☐   57 + 22 = ☐

68 + 26 = ☐   45 + 37 = ☐

465 + 4 = ☐

353 + 6 = ☐

272 + 7 = ☐

756 + 7 = ☐

Fact families

Here is a fact family for 8 + 6 = 14.

- 8 + 6 = 14
- 14 − 6 = 8

- 6 + 8 = 14
- 14 − 8 = 6

Complete the following fact families:

- 8 + 9 = 17

- ___ − ___ = ___

- ___ + ___ = ___

- ___ − ___ = ___

- 9 + 5 = 14

- ___ − ___ = ___

- ___ + ___ = ___

- ___ − ___ = ___

- 5 + 7 = 12

- ___ − ___ = ___

- ___ + ___ = ___

- ___ − ___ = ___

Here is a fact family for 13 + 7 = 20.

- **13 + 7 = 20**
- **20 − 7 = 13**
- **7 + 13 = 20**
- **20 − 13 = 7**

Complete the following fact families:

- **8 + 5 = 13**
- ___ − ___ = ___

- ___ + ___ = ___
- ___ − ___ = ___

- **13 + 3 = 16**
- ___ − ___ = ___

- ___ + ___ = ___
- ___ − ___ = ___

- **11 + 4 = 15**
- ___ − ___ = ___

- ___ + ___ = ___
- ___ − ___ = ___

Penguin subtraction

Work out the subtractions and write the answers on the penguins.

6 − 3 =

8 − 7 =

11 − 2 =

13 − 7 =

15 − 9 =

16 − 8 =

9 − 4 =

10 − 6 =

Missing numbers

Complete the subtractions by filling in the missing numbers.

3 – ☐ = 0   21 – ☐ = 14

☐ – 4 = 8   15 – 5 = ☐

17 – ☐ = 9   12 – ☐ = 9

☐ – 9 = 0   18 – 10 = ☐

5 – ☐ = 4   20 – ☐ = 10

Bubble subtractions

Complete the subtractions by filling in the missing numbers.

$11 - \boxed{} = 5$

$\boxed{} - 5 = 7$

$\boxed{} - 7 = 6$

$\boxed{} - 4 = 8$

$14 - \boxed{} = 9$

$\boxed{} - 5 = 17$

$\boxed{} - 7 = 16$

Subtraction in space

Work out the subtractions and write the answers in the boxes.

79 – 6 = ☐   88 – 5 = ☐

99 – 8 = ☐   56 – 4 = ☐

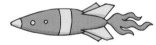

49 – 3 = ☐   37 – 5 = ☐

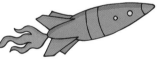

78 – 4 = ☐   29 – 8 = ☐

Subtraction is magic!

Complete the subtractions by taking a one digit number away from a two digit number. Write your answers in the boxes.

49 – 5 =

37 – 6 =

55 – 3 =

28 – 6 =

67 – 4 =

23 – 9 =

76 – 8 =

54 – 5 =

Double digits

Complete the subtractions by taking a two digit number away from another two digit number. Write your answers in the boxes.

79 − 16 = ☐   83 − 19 = ☐

27 − 11 = ☐   56 − 12 = ☐

49 − 13 = ☐   57 − 17 = ☐

23 − 13 = ☐   40 − 28 = ☐

Fun with subtractions

Solve these problems and write the answers in the boxes.

Take **4** bananas away from these monkeys. How many bananas are left?

If **3** parrots fly away how many parrots are left?

Colour **5** of these balloons. How many are left white?

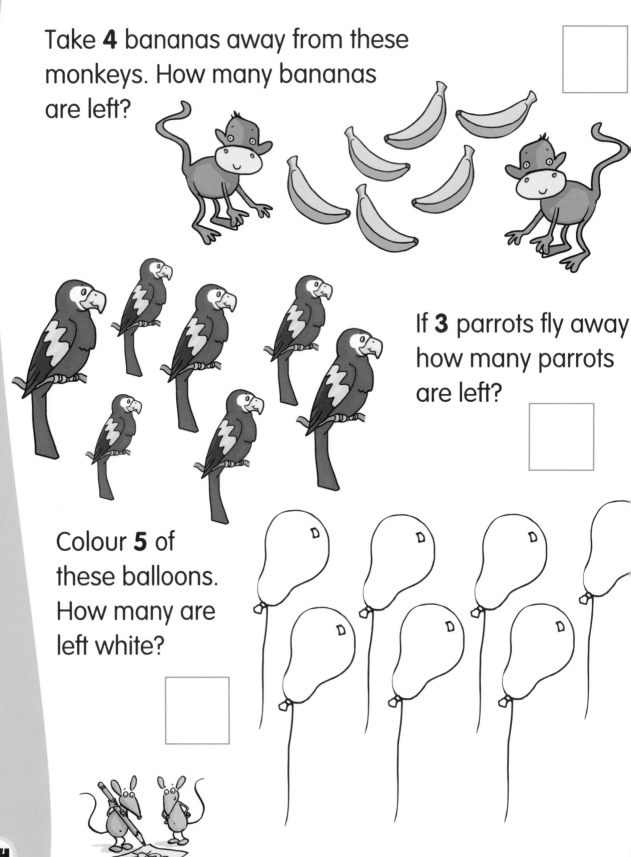

A rabbit eats **4** carrots. How many carrots are left?

Draw **8** lit candles on this cake.

If Molly blows out **3** candles, how many lit candles are left?

Butterfly subtractions

Do the subtractions and write the answers in the boxes.

90 – 6 = ☐   60 – 3 = ☐

40 – 4 = ☐   30 – 8 = ☐

50 – 5 = ☐   44 – 7 = ☐

33 – 5 = ☐   52 – 7 = ☐

78 − 9 =

63 − 6 =

83 − 9 =

14 − 12 =

55 − 16 =

77 − 17 =

28 − 13 =

84 − 18 =

Super subtractions

Try taking a one digit number away from a three digit number.
Write your answers in the boxes.

537 – 5 = $\boxed{}$ 648 – 6 = $\boxed{}$

354 – 3 = $\boxed{}$ 192 – 6 = $\boxed{}$

746 – 8 = $\boxed{}$ 371 – 5 = $\boxed{}$

823 – 8 = $\boxed{}$ 342 – 7 = $\boxed{}$

185 – 9 = $\boxed{}$ 203 – 8 = $\boxed{}$

Subtraction test

Now take the subtraction test. Do the subtractions and write the answers in the boxes.

$13 - 8 =$ ⬚ $11 - 1 =$ ⬚

$15 - 9 =$ ⬚ $18 - 6 =$ ⬚

A boy has **8** sweets and he eats **5**. How many sweets does he have left? ⬚

$14 - 12 =$ ⬚ $17 - 8 =$ ⬚

$22 - 10 =$ ⬚ $24 - 5 =$ ⬚

25 rabbits are sitting in a field and **9** run away. How many rabbits are left? ⬚

Subtraction test 2

29 − 7 = ☐   37 − 6 = ☐

58 − 3 = ☐   98 − 8 = ☐

48 − 12 = ☐   27 − 15 = ☐

65 − 16 = ☐   39 − 19 = ☐

423 − 4 = ☐

275 − 3 = ☐

739 − 8 = ☐

456 − 9 = ☐

Answers

Number bonds to 10

+ **3** = 10
+ **2** = 10
+ **1** = 10
+ **6** = 10
+ **5** = 10

+ **3** = 10
4 + **6** = 10
9 + **1** = 10
5 + **5** = 10
2 + **8** = 10

Addition on the farm

5 + 7 = 12
4 + 4 = 8
7 + 7 = 14
4 + 3 = **7**
10 + 10 = 20
+ 9 = 10

2 + **2** = 4
7 + 9 = **16**
12 + 7 = 19
0 + 11 = 11
8 + **13** = 21
18 + 12 = **30**
8 + 7 = 15
9 + 8 = 17

Alien addition

15 + 3 = **18**
16 + 2 = **18**
11 + 3 = **14**
18 + 7 = **25**
15 + 9 = **24**
13 + 4 = **17**

26 + 7 = **33**
23 + 9 = **32**
18 + 5 = **23**
91 + 8 = **99**
48 + 3 = **51**
35 + 6 = **41**
67 + 7 = **74**
55 + 6 = **61**

Missing numbers

34 + 6 = **40**
83 + 7 = **90**
77 + 3 = **80**
78 + 4 = **82**
53 + 9 = **62**
23 + 6 = **29**
45 + 7 = **52**
88 + 5 = **93**
13 + 9 = **22**

Adding 10s

5 + 8 = **13**
6 + 3 = **9**
2 + 6 = **8**
5 + 1 = **6**
7 + 5 = **12**
8 + 3 = **11**

50 + 80 = **130**
60 + 30 = **90**
20 + 60 = **80**
50 + 10 = **60**
70 + 50 = **120**
80 + 30 = **110**

Adding 100s

300 + 200 = **500**
400 + 300 = **700**
200 + 700 = **900**
100 + 700 = **800**
200 + 500 = **700**
400 + 500 = **900**

Match the answers

6 + 2 = **8**
15 + 3 = **18**
12 + 7 = **19**
10 + 40 = **50**
12 + 8 = **20**
20 + 50 = **70**

Double digits

35 + 22 = **57**
43 + 36 = **79**
25 + 42 = **67**
65 + 24 = **89**
52 + 34 = **86**
76 + 22 = **98**
23 + 51 = **74**
43 + 17 = **60**
67 + 28 = **95**
37 + 51 = **88**

It all adds up

178 + 45 = **223**
259 + 52 = **311**
444 + 63 = **507**
153 + 70 = **223**
456 + 16 = **472**
322 + 26 = **348**
244 + 55 = **299**
101 + 23 = **124**

Addition test

11 + 2 = **13**
6 + 7 = **13**
10 + 5 = **15**
3 + 12 = **15**
12 sweets
21 + 6 = **27**
20 + 8 = **28**
17 + 7 = **24**
12 + 6 = **18**
17 eyes

13 + 12 = **25**
20 + 16 = **36**
34 + 23 = **57**
42 + 16 = **58**
48 + 31 = **79**
57 + 22 = **79**
68 + 26 = **94**
45 + 37 = **82**
465 + 4 = **469**
353 + 6 = **359**
272 + 7 = **279**
756 + 7 = **763**

Answers

Fact families

8 + 9 = 17	9 + 8 = 17
17 − 9 = 8	17 − 8 = 9
9 + 5 = 14	5 + 9 = 14
14 − 5 = 9	14 − 9 = 5
5 + 7 = 12	7 + 5 = 12
12 − 7 = 5	12 − 5 = 7
8 + 5 = 13	5 + 8 = 13
13 − 5 = 8	13 − 8 = 5
13 + 3 = 16	3 + 13 = 16
16 − 3 = 13	16 − 13 = 3
11 + 4 = 15	4 + 11 = 15
15 − 4 = 11	15 − 11 = 4

Penguin subtraction

6 − 3 = **3**
8 − 7 = **1**
11 − 2 = **9**
13 − 7 = **6**
15 − 9 = **6**
16 − 8 = **8**
9 − 4 = **5**
10 − 6 = **4**

Missing numbers

3 − **3** = 0
21 − **7** = 14
12 − 4 = 8
15 − 5 = **10**
17 − **8** = 9
12 − **3** = 9
9 − 9 = 0
18 − 10 = **8**
5 − **1** = 4
20 − **10** = 10

Bubble subtractions

11 − **6** = 5
12 − 5 = 7
13 − 7 = 6
12 − 4 = 8
14 − **5** = 9
22 − 5 = 17
23 − 7 = 16

Subtraction in space

79 − 6 = **73**
88 − 5 = **83**
99 − 8 = **91**
56 − 4 = **52**
49 − 3 = **46**
37 − 5 = **32**
78 − 4 = **74**
29 − 8 = **21**

Subtraction is magic!

49 − 5 = **44**
37 − 6 = **31**
55 − 3 = **52**
28 − 6 = **22**
67 − 4 = **63**
23 − 9 = **14**
76 − 8 = **68**
54 − 5 = **49**

Double digits

79 − 16 = **63**
83 − 19 = **64**
27 − 11 = **16**
56 − 12 = **44**
49 − 13 = **36**
57 − 17 = **40**
23 − 13 = **10**
40 − 28 = **12**

Fun with subtractions

2 bananas
4 parrots
2 balloons
4 carrots
5 candles

Butterfly subtractions

90 − 6 = **84**
60 − 3 = **57**
40 − 4 = **36**
30 − 8 = **22**
50 − 5 = **45**
44 − 7 = **37**
33 − 5 = **28**
52 − 7 = **45**
78 − 9 = **69**
63 − 6 = **57**
83 − 9 = **74**

14 − 12 = **2**
55 − 16 = **39**
77 − 17 = **60**
28 − 13 = **15**
84 − 18 = **66**

Super subtraction

537 − 5 = **532**
648 − 6 = **642**
354 − 3 = **351**
192 − 6 = **186**
746 − 8 = **738**
371 − 5 = **366**
823 − 8 = **815**
342 − 7 = **335**
185 − 9 = **176**
203 − 8 = **195**

Subtraction test

13 − 8 = **5**
11 − 1 = **10**
15 − 9 = **6**
18 − 6 = **12**
3 sweets
14 − 12 = **2**
17 − 8 = **9**
22 − 10 = **12**
24 − 5 = **19**
16 rabbits

Subtraction test 2

29 − 7 = **22**
37 − 6 = **31**
58 − 3 = **55**
98 − 8 = **90**
48 − 12 = **36**
27 − 15 = **12**
65 − 16 = **49**
39 − 19 = **20**
423 − 4 = **419**
275 − 3 = **272**
739 − 8 = **731**
456 − 9 = **447**

Multiplying and Dividing

In Year Two (age 7+) your child is expected to be able to:

• Recall and use multiplication and division facts for the 2, 5 and 10 times tables, including recognising odd and even numbers.

• Calculate the answers to multiplication and division statements using multiplication (x), division (÷) and equals (=) signs.

• Show that multiplication of 2 numbers can be done in any order, but that division of one number cannot be done in any order.

• Solve multiplication and division problems using materials, array, repeated addition, mental methods and multiplication and division facts, including problems in context.

Multiplication tables 1 – 6

Complete the multiplication tables below.
Try to learn them off by heart.

x1

1 x 1 = 1

2 x 1 = 2

3 x 1 = 3

4 x 1 = 4

5 x 1 = 5

6 x 1 = ☐

7 x 1 = 7

8 x 1 = 8

9 x 1 = 9

10 x 1 = ☐

11 x 1 = 11

12 x 1 = 12

x2

1 x 2 = 2

2 x 2 = 4

3 x 2 = 6

4 x 2 = ☐

5 x 2 = 10

6 x 2 = 12

7 x 2 = 14

8 x 2 = 16

9 x 2 = 18

10 x 2 = 20

11 x 2 = 22

12 x 2 = ☐

x3

1 x 3 = 3

2 x 3 = 6

3 x 3 = 9

4 x 3 = ☐

5 x 3 = 15

6 x 3 = 18

7 x 3 = 21

8 x 3 = ☐

9 x 3 = 27

10 x 3 = 30

11 x 3 = 33

12 x 3 = 36

x4

1 x 4 = 4

2 x 4 = 8

3 x 4 = 12

4 x 4 = 16

5 x 4 = ☐

6 x 4 = 24

7 x 4 = 28

8 x 4 = 32

9 x 4 = ☐

10 x 4 = 40

11 x 4 = 44

12 x 4 = 48

x5

1 x 5 = 5

2 x 5 = 10

3 x 5 = 15

4 x 5 = 20

5 x 5 = ☐

6 x 5 = 30

7 x 5 = 35

8 x 5 = 40

9 x 5 = 45

10 x 5 = ☐

11 x 5 = 55

12 x 5 = 60

x6

1 x 6 = 6

2 x 6 = ☐

3 x 6 = 18

4 x 6 = 24

5 x 6 = 30

6 x 6 = 36

7 x 6 = 42

8 x 6 = 48

9 x 6 = ☐

10 x 6 = 60

11 x 6 = 66

12 x 6 = 72

Multiplication tables 7 – 12

Complete the multiplication tables below.
Try to learn them off by heart.

x7

1 x 7 = ☐
2 x 7 = 14
3 x 7 = 21
4 x 7 = 28
5 x 7 = 35
6 x 7 = ☐
7 x 7 = 49
8 x 7 = 56
9 x 7 = 63
10 x 7 = 70
11 x 7 = 77
12 x 7 = 84

x8

1 x 8 = 8
2 x 8 = 16
3 x 8 = 24
4 x 8 = 32
5 x 8 = 40
6 x 8 = 48
7 x 8 = ☐
8 x 8 = 64
9 x 8 = 72
10 x 8 = ☐
11 x 8 = 88
12 x 8 = 96

x9

1 x 9 = 9
2 x 9 = 18
3 x 9 = 27
4 x 9 = 36
5 x 9 = ☐
6 x 9 = 54
7 x 9 = 63
8 x 9 = 72
9 x 9 = ☐
10 x 9 = 90
11 x 9 = 99
12 x 9 = 108

x10

1 × 10 = 10

2 × 10 = 20

3 × 10 = 30

4 × 10 = ☐

5 × 10 = 50

6 × 10 = 60

7 × 10 = 70

8 × 10 = 80

9 × 10 = 90

10 × 10 = ☐

11 × 10 = 110

12 × 10 = 120

x11

1 × 11 = 11

2 × 11 = 22

3 × 11 = 33

4 × 11 = ☐

5 × 11 = 55

6 × 11 = 66

7 × 11 = 77

8 × 11 = 88

9 × 11 = ☐

10 × 11 = 110

11 × 11 = 121

12 × 11 = 132

x12

1 × 12 = 12

2 × 12 = ☐

3 × 12 = 36

4 × 12 = 48

5 × 12 = 60

6 × 12 = ☐

7 × 12 = 84

8 × 12 = 96

9 × 12 = 108

10 × 12 = 120

11 × 12 = 132

12 × 12 = 144

Multiplication problems

Solve these multiplication problems and write your answers in the boxes.

a. 4 × 2 = ☐   11 × 2 = ☐

b. **6** bicycles have **2** wheels each. How many wheels are there altogether? ☐

c. 3 × 5 = ☐   9 × 5 = ☐

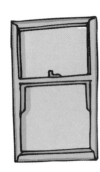

d. **7** houses have **5** windows each. How many windows are there altogether? ☐

e. 5 × 10 = ☐   8 × 10 = ☐

f. **12** children have **10** fingers each. How many fingers are there altogether? ☐

g. 5 × 3 = ☐   11 × 3 = ☐

h. **7** tricycles have **3** wheels each.
How many wheels are there
altogether? ☐

i. 7 × 4 = ☐   9 × 4 = ☐

j. **12** ladybirds have **4** spots each.
How many spots are there
altogether? ☐

k. 4 × 6 = ☐   11 × 6 = ☐

l. **8** rabbits each eat **6** carrots.
How many carrots have the
rabbits eaten altogether? ☐

Alien multiplication

Solve these alien multiplication problems and write your answers in the boxes.

a. 8 × 7 = ☐   3 × 7 = ☐

b. **11** aliens have **7** arms each. How many arms are there altogether? ☐

c. 8 × 8 = ☐   6 × 8 = ☐

d. **12** aliens have **8** toes each. How many toes are there altogether? ☐

e. 9 × 9 = ☐   6 × 9 = ☐

f. **4** aliens have **9** eyes each. How many eyes are there altogether? ☐

What's the answer?

Solve these multiplication problems and write your answers in the boxes.

a. **7 x 11 =** [ ] **12 x 11 =** [ ]

b. **4 x 11 =** [ ] **8 x 11 =** [ ]

c. There are **11** football players in a team and there are **6** teams. How many football players are there altogether? [ ]

d. **4 x 12 =** [ ] **9 x 12 =** [ ]

e. **7 x 12 =** [ ] **3 x 12 =** [ ]

f. **8** girls have **12** sweets each. How many sweets are there altogether? [ ]

Square numbers

A square number is a number which is multiplied by itself.
e.g. The **square of 2** is the same as **2 x 2**.
Solve these square numbers and write your answers in the boxes.

$7 \times 7 =$ ☐

$12 \times 12 =$ ☐

$9 \times 9 =$ ☐

$3 \times 3 =$ ☐

$8 \times 8 =$ ☐

$6 \times 6 =$ ☐

$1 \times 1 =$ ☐

$4 \times 4 =$ ☐

$2 \times 2 =$ ☐

$10 \times 10 =$ ☐

$5 \times 5 =$ ☐

$11 \times 11 =$ ☐

Challenge: Put the square numbers above in order, lowest to highes

_ _ _ _ _ _ _ _ _ _ _ _ _ _ _

_ _ _ _ _ _ _ _ _ _ _ _ _ _ _

What do you notice about the difference (the gap)
between each of the square numbers above?

_ _ _ _ _ _ _ _ _ _ _ _ _ _ _

_ _ _ _ _ _ _ _ _ _ _ _ _ _ _

Short multiplication

Practise multiplying a two digit number by a one digit number.
Use the space to show your workings.

g. **17 × 4 = 68**

$$\begin{array}{r} 17 \\ \times\ \ 4 \\ \hline 6\ 8 \\ \end{array}$$
2

21 × 4 =

32 × 3 =

19 × 5 =

13 × 6 =

12 × 7 =

More short multiplication

Practise multiplying a two digit number by a one digit number. Use the space to show your workings.

e.g. **34 × 5 =** | **170**

```
    3 4
  ×   5
  -----
  1 7 0
    2
```

29 × 4 =

38 × 3 =

53 × 5 =

42 × 6 =

17 × 7 =

Opposites and inverse

Using the multiplications below, work out the inverses (divisions).
Don't forget, you need to use all of the same numbers!

e.g. **3 x 5 = 15** SO **15 ÷ 3 = 5**
or **15 ÷ 5 = 3**

a. **3 x 4 = 12** SO ☐ ÷ ☐ = ☐

b. **5 x 6 = 30** SO ☐ ÷ ☐ = ☐

c. **4 x 7 = 28** SO ☐ ÷ ☐ = ☐

d. **11 x 9 = 99** SO ☐ ÷ ☐ = ☐

Multiplication facts

Using the example, work out the multiplications below.
Write your answers in the boxes.
What do you notice?

e.g.   **2 x 3 = 6** SO **20 x 3 = 60**

$$5 \times 4 = 20 \text{ SO } 50 \times 4 = \boxed{}$$

$$9 \times 5 = 45 \text{ SO } 90 \times 5 = \boxed{}$$

$$7 \times 8 = 56 \text{ SO } 70 \times 8 = \boxed{}$$

$$6 \times 7 = 42 \text{ SO } 6 \times 70 = \boxed{}$$

$3 \times 7 = 21$ so $30 \times 7 =$ ☐

$4 \times 6 = 24$ so $4 \times 60 =$ ☐

$7 \times 9 = 63$ so $70 \times 9 =$ ☐

and $70 \times 90 =$ ☐

$11 \times 8 = 88$ so $110 \times 8 =$ ☐

and $110 \times 80 =$ ☐

Test time!

Are you ready to test yourself? Have a go at these questions and see how many you get right!

a. 2 x 2 = ▢ **b.** 5 x 8 = ▢

c. 4 x 5 = ▢ **d.** 6 x 7 = ▢

e. 8 x 8 = ▢ **f.** 11 x 2 = ▢

g. 1 x 3 = ▢ **h.** 10 x 11 = ▢

i. 13 children have **3** toys each. How many toys are there altogether? ▢

j. What is the square of **3**? ▢

k. What is the square of **9**? ▢

l. 60 x 5 = ☐

m. 43 x 4 = ☐

n. 52 x 3 = ☐

o. 37 x 5 = ☐

p. 8 x 3 = 24 so 80 x 3 = ☐

q. 11 x 11 = 121 so 11 x 110 = ☐

r. and 110 x 110 = ☐

Division tables 1 – 6

Complete the division tables below.
Try to learn them off by heart.

÷1

1 ÷ 1 = 1

2 ÷ 1 = 2

3 ÷ 1 = 3

4 ÷ 1 = 4

5 ÷ 1 = 5

6 ÷ 1 = ☐

7 ÷ 1 = 7

8 ÷ 1 = 8

9 ÷ 1 = 9

10 ÷ 1 = 10

11 ÷ 1 = ☐

12 ÷ 1 = 12

÷2

2 ÷ 2 = 1

4 ÷ 2 = 2

6 ÷ 2 = 3

8 ÷ 2 = ☐

10 ÷ 2 = 5

12 ÷ 2 = 6

14 ÷ 2 = 7

16 ÷ 2 = 8

☐ ÷ 2 = 9

20 ÷ 2 = 10

22 ÷ 2 = 11

24 ÷ 2 = 12

÷3

3 ÷ 3 = 1

6 ÷ 3 = 2

9 ÷ 3 = 3

12 ÷ 3 = ☐

15 ÷ 3 = 5

18 ÷ 3 = 6

21 ÷ 3 = 7

24 ÷ 3 = 8

☐ ÷ 3 = 9

30 ÷ 3 = 10

33 ÷ 3 = 11

36 ÷ 3 = 12

50

÷4

4 ÷ 4 = 1

8 ÷ 4 = 2

12 ÷ 4 = 3

16 ÷ 4 = ☐

20 ÷ 4 = 5

24 ÷ 4 = 6

28 ÷ 4 = 7

☐ ÷ 4 = 8

36 ÷ 4 = 9

40 ÷ 4 = 10

44 ÷ 4 = 11

48 ÷ 4 = 12

÷5

5 ÷ 5 = 1

10 ÷ 5 = 2

15 ÷ 5 = 3

20 ÷ 5 = 4

25 ÷ 5 = 5

☐ ÷ 5 = 6

35 ÷ 5 = 7

40 ÷ 5 = ☐

45 ÷ 5 = 9

50 ÷ 5 = 10

55 ÷ 5 = 11

60 ÷ 5 = 12

÷6

6 ÷ 6 = 1

12 ÷ 6 = 2

☐ ÷ 6 = 3

24 ÷ 6 = 4

30 ÷ 6 = 5

36 ÷ 6 = 6

42 ÷ 6 = 7

48 ÷ 6 = 8

54 ÷ 6 = ☐

60 ÷ 6 = 10

66 ÷ 6 = 11

72 ÷ 6 = 12

Division tables 7 - 12

Complete the division tables below.
Try to learn them off by heart.

÷7

$7 \div 7 = 1$

$14 \div 7 = 2$

$\boxed{} \div 7 = 3$

$28 \div 7 = 4$

$35 \div 7 = 5$

$42 \div 7 = \boxed{}$

$49 \div 7 = 7$

$56 \div 7 = 8$

$63 \div 7 = 9$

$70 \div 7 = 10$

$77 \div 7 = 11$

$84 \div 7 = 12$

÷8

$8 \div 8 = 1$

$16 \div 8 = 2$

$24 \div 8 = 3$

$32 \div 8 = 4$

$40 \div 8 = \boxed{}$

$48 \div 8 = 6$

$56 \div 8 = 7$

$64 \div 8 = 8$

$72 \div 8 = 9$

$80 \div 8 = 10$

$88 \div 8 = 11$

$\boxed{} \div 8 = 12$

÷9

$9 \div 9 = 1$

$18 \div 9 = 2$

$27 \div 9 = 3$

$36 \div 9 = 4$

$45 \div 9 = 5$

$54 \div 9 = \boxed{}$

$63 \div 9 = 7$

$72 \div 9 = 8$

$\boxed{} \div 9 = 9$

$90 \div 9 = 10$

$99 \div 9 = 11$

$108 \div 9 = 12$

÷10

10 ÷ 10 = 1

20 ÷ 10 = 2

30 ÷ 10 = 3

☐ ÷ 10 = 4

50 ÷ 10 = 5

60 ÷ 10 = 6

70 ÷ 10 = 7

80 ÷ 10 = ☐

90 ÷ 10 = 9

100 ÷ 10 = 10

110 ÷ 10 = 11

120 ÷ 10 = 12

÷11

11 ÷ 11 = 1

22 ÷ 11 = 2

33 ÷ 11 = 3

44 ÷ 11 = 4

55 ÷ 11 = ☐

66 ÷ 11 = 6

77 ÷ 11 = 7

88 ÷ 11 = 8

☐ ÷ 11 = 9

110 ÷ 11 = 10

121 ÷ 11 = 11

132 ÷ 11 = 12

÷12

12 ÷ 12 = 1

24 ÷ 12 = 2

36 ÷ 12 = ☐

48 ÷ 12 = 4

60 ÷ 12 = 5

72 ÷ 12 = 6

84 ÷ 12 = 7

☐ ÷ 12 = 8

108 ÷ 12 = 9

120 ÷ 12 = 10

132 ÷ 12 = 11

144 ÷ 12 = 12

Division precision

Solve these dividing problems and write your answers in the boxes.

a. 8 ÷ 2 = ☐   14 ÷ 2 = ☐

b. Share **12** books equally between **2** children. How many books each? ☐

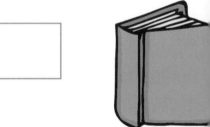

c. 15 ÷ 5 = ☐   40 ÷ 5 = ☐

d. Share **35** carrots equally between **5** rabbits. How many carrots each? ☐

e. 50 ÷ 10 = ☐   80 ÷ 10 = ☐

f. Share **120** bananas equally between **10** monkeys. How many bananas each? ☐

g. $12 \div 3 = \boxed{}$ $21 \div 3 = \boxed{}$

h. Share **18** balloons equally between **3** clowns. How many balloons each? $\boxed{}$

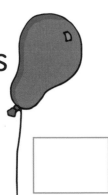

. $12 \div 4 = \boxed{}$ $40 \div 4 = \boxed{}$

. Share **36** acorns equally between **4** squirrels. How many acorns each? $\boxed{}$

k. $54 \div 6 = \boxed{}$ $48 \div 6 = \boxed{}$

. Share **72** berries equally between **6** birds. How many berries each? $\boxed{}$

Division problems

Solve these division problems and write your answers in the boxes.

a. $28 \div 7 = \boxed{}$ $56 \div 7 = \boxed{}$

b. Share **84** biscuits equally between **7** children. How many biscuits each? $\boxed{}$

c. $16 \div 8 = \boxed{}$ $64 \div 8 = \boxed{}$

d. Share **72** apples equally between **8** horses. How many apples each? $\boxed{}$

e. $54 \div 9 = \boxed{}$ $72 \div 9 = \boxed{}$

f. Share **63** stickers equally between **9** boys. How many stickers does each boy have? $\boxed{}$

g. $132 \div 11 =$ ☐ $77 \div 11 =$ ☐

h. $99 \div 11 =$ ☐ $33 \div 11 =$ ☐

i. **121** football players are split equally into **11** teams. How many players are there in each team? ☐

j. $48 \div 12 =$ ☐ $96 \div 12 =$ ☐

k. $72 \div 12 =$ ☐ $36 \div 12 =$ ☐

l. Share **60** bees equally between **12** beehives. How many bees in each? ☐

Fact attack!

Using the example, work out these division problems. Write your answers in the boxes.

e.g. $35 \div 5 = 7$ SO $350 \div 5 = 70$

$50 \div 5 = 10$ SO $500 \div 5 =$ ☐

$45 \div 5 = 9$ SO $450 \div 5 =$ ☐

$8 \div 2 = 4$ SO $80 \div 2 =$ ☐

$15 \div 3 = 5$ SO $150 \div 3 =$ ☐

$48 \div 12 = 4$ so $480 \div 12 =$

$21 \div 7 = 3$ so $210 \div 7 =$

$70 \div 10 = 7$ so $700 \div 10 =$

and $700 \div 100 =$

$54 \div 9 = 6$ so $540 \div 9 =$

and $540 \div 90 =$

Short division

Practise dividing a two digit number by a one digit number.
Use the space to show your workings.

e.g. **72 ÷ 6 =** 12   **45 ÷ 5 =**

$$
\begin{array}{r}
1\ 2 \\
6\ \overline{\smash{)}7\ ^1 2}
\end{array}
$$

99 ÷ 9 =   **77 ÷ 7 =**

Share **58** sweets between **8** children.

How many sweets
does each child get?

How many sweets
are left over?

Test time!

Are you ready to **test yourself**? Have a go at these questions and see how many you can get right!

a.　6 ÷ 3 = ☐　　　b. 64 ÷ 8 = ☐

c. 14 ÷ 2 = ☐　　　d. 40 ÷ 4 = ☐

e. 25 ÷ 5 = ☐　　　f.　5 ÷ 5 = ☐

g. 27 ÷ 9 = ☐　　　h. 21 ÷ 3 = ☐

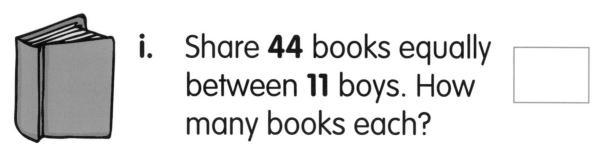

i.　Share **44** books equally between **11** boys. How many books each? ☐

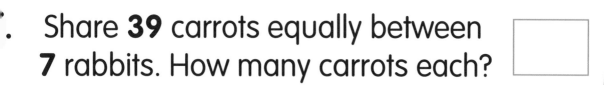

j.　Share **39** carrots equally between **7** rabbits. How many carrots each? ☐

k.　How many carrots are left over? ☐

$20 \div 5 = 4$ so $200 \div 5 =$

$72 \div 9 = 8$ so $720 \div 9 =$

 and $720 \div 90 =$

$88 \div 8 =$

$90 \div 10 =$

$84 \div 7 =$

$25 \div 5 =$

Answers

Multiplication tables

6 x 1 = **6**	10 x 1 = **10**
4 x 2 = **8**	12 x 2 = **24**
4 x 3 = **12**	8 x 3 = **24**
5 x 4 = **20**	9 x 4 = **36**
5 x 5 = **25**	10 x 5 = **50**
2 x 6 = **12**	9 x 6 = **54**
1 x 7 = **7**	6 x 7 = **42**
7 x 8 = **56**	10 x 8 = **80**
5 x 9 = **45**	9 x 9 = **81**
4 x 10 = **40**	10 x 10 = **100**
4 x 11 = **44**	9 x 11 = **99**
2 x 12 = **24**	6 x 12 = **72**

Multiplication problems

a. 4 x 2 = **8**   11 x 2 = **22**

b. **12** wheels

c. 3 x 5 = **15**   9 x 5 = **45**

d. **35** windows

e. 5 x 10 = **50**   8 x 10 = **80**

f. **120** fingers

g. 5 x 3 = **15**   11 x 3 = **33**

h. **21** wheels

i. 7 x 4 = **28**   9 x 4 = **36**

j. **48** spots

k. 4 x 6 = **24**   11 x 6 = **66**

l. **48** carrots

Alien multiplication

a. 8 x 7 = **56**   3 x 7 = **21**

b. **77** arms

c. 8 x 8 = **64**   6 x 8 = **48**

d. **96** toes

e. 9 x 9 = **81**   6 x 9 = **54**

f. **36** eyes

What's the answer?

a. 7 x 11 = **77**   12 x 11 = **132**

b. 4 x 11 = **44**   8 x 11 = **88**

c. **66** football players

d. 4 x 12 = **48**   9 x 12 = **108**

e. 7 x 12 = **84**   3 x 12 = **36**

f. **96** sweets

Square numbers

7 x 7 = **49**	1 x 1 = **1**
12 x 12 = **144**	4 x 4 = **16**
9 x 9 = **81**	2 x 2 = **4**
3 x 3 = **9**	10 x 10 = **100**
8 x 8 = **64**	5 x 5 = **25**
6 x 6 = **36**	11 x 11 = **121**

Challenge **1, 4, 9, 16, 25, 36, 49, 64, 81, 100, 121, 144**

The gaps increase by **3, 5, 7, 9, 11, 13, 15, 17, 19, 21, 23**

Short multiplication

21 x 4 = **84**

32 x 3 = **96**

19 x 5 = **95**

13 x 6 = **78**

12 x 7 = **84**

More short multiplication

29 x 4 = **116**

38 x 3 = **114**

53 x 5 = **265**

42 x 6 = **252**

17 x 7 = **119**

Opposites and inverse

a. 12 ÷ 3 = **4**   or   12 ÷ 4 = **3**

b. 30 ÷ 5 = **6**   or   30 ÷ 6 = **5**

c. 28 ÷ 4 = **7**   or   28 ÷ 7 = **4**

d. 99 ÷ 9 = **11**   or   99 ÷ 11 = **9**

Answers

Multiplication facts

50 x 4 = **200**

90 x 5 = **450**

70 x 8 = **560**

6 x 70 = **420**

30 x 7 = **210**

4 x 60 = **240**

70 x 9 = **630**

70 x 90 = **6,300**

110 x 8 = **880**

110 x 80 = **8,800**

Test time!

a. 2 x 2 = **4**

b. 5 x 8 = **40**

c. 4 x 5 = **20**

d. 6 x 7 = **42**

e. 8 x 8 = **64**

f. 11 x 2 = **22**

g. 1 x 3 = **3**

h. 10 x 11 = **110**

i. **39** toys

j. **9**

k. **81**

l. **300**

m. **172**

n. **156**

o. **185**

p. 80 x 30 = **240**

q. 11 x 110 = **1,210**

r. 110 x 110 = **12,100**

Division tables

6 ÷ 1 = **6**   11 ÷ 1 = **11**

8 ÷ 2 = **4**   18 ÷ 2 = 9

12 ÷ 3 = **4**   27 ÷ 3 = 9

16 ÷ 4 = **4**   32 ÷ 4 = 8

30 ÷ 5 = 6   40 ÷ 5 = **8**

18 ÷ 6 = 3   54 ÷ 6 = **9**

21 ÷ 7 = 3   42 ÷ 7 = **6**

40 ÷ 8 = **5**   96 ÷ 8 = 12

54 ÷ 9 = **6**   81 ÷ 9 = 9

40 ÷ 10 = 4   80 ÷ 10 = **8**

55 ÷ 11 = **5**   99 ÷ 11 = 9

36 ÷ 12 = **3**   96 ÷ 12 = 8

Division precision

a. 8 ÷ 2 = **4**   14 ÷ 2 = **7**

b. **6** books

c. 15 ÷ 5 = **3**   40 ÷ 5 = **8**

d. **7** carrots

e. 50 ÷ 10 = **5**   80 ÷ 10 = **8**

f. **12** bananas

g. 12 ÷ 3 = **4**   21 ÷ 3 = **7**

h. **6** balloons

i. 12 ÷ 4 = **3**   40 ÷ 4 = **10**

j. **9** acorns

k. 54 ÷ 6 = **9**   48 ÷ 6 = **8**

l. **12** berries

Division problems

a. 28 ÷ 7 = **4**   56 ÷ 7 = 8

b. **12** biscuits

c. 16 ÷ 8 = **2**   64 ÷ 8 = 8

d. **9** apples

e. 54 ÷ 9 = **6**   72 ÷ 9 = 8

f. **7** stickers

g. 132 ÷ 11 = **12**   77 ÷ 11 = **7**

h. 99 ÷ 11 = **9**   33 ÷ 11 = **3**

i. **11** players

j. 48 ÷ 12 = **4**   96 ÷ 12 = 8

k. 72 ÷ 12 = **6**   36 ÷ 12 = **3**

l. **5** bees

Fact attack!

500 ÷ 5 = **100**

450 ÷ 5 = **90**

80 ÷ 2 = **40**

150 ÷ 3 = **50**

480 ÷ 12 = **40**

210 ÷ 7 = **30**

700 ÷ 10 = **70**

700 ÷ 100 = **7**

540 ÷ 9 = **60**

540 ÷ 90 = **6**

Short division

45 ÷ 5 = **9**

99 ÷ 9 = **11**

77 ÷ 7 = **11**

7 sweets each

2 sweets left over

Test time!

a. 6 ÷ 3 = **2**

b. 64 ÷ 8 = **8**

c. 14 ÷ 2 = **7**

d. 40 ÷ 4 = **10**

e. 25 ÷ 5 = **5**

f. 5 ÷ 5 = **1**

g. 27 ÷ 9 = **3**

h. 21 ÷ 3 = **7**

i. **4** books

j. **5** carrots each

k. **4** carrots left over

Test time 2!

200 ÷ 5 = **40**

720 ÷ 9 = **80**

720 ÷ 90 = **8**

88 ÷ 8 = **11**

90 ÷ 10 = **9**

84 ÷ 7 = **12**

25 ÷ 5 = **5**

Mental Maths

In Year Two (age 7+) your child is expected to be able to:

• Count in steps of 2, 3 and 5 from 0 and in 10s from any number forward and backward.

• Compare and order numbers from 0 up to 100.

• Read and write numbers to at least 100 in numerals and in words.

• Use place value and number facts to solve problems.

• Solve problems with addition and subtraction by applying their increasing knowledge of mental and written methods.

• Recall and use addition and subtraction facts to 20 fluently, and use related facts up to 100.

• Add and subtract numbers mentally.

• Recall and use multiplication and division facts for the 2, 5 and 10 times tables.

• Solve problems involving multiplication and division using mental methods, including problems in context.

Get ready!

As a warm up, solve these problems by adding the numbers up in your head. Say the answers aloud, then write them in the boxes.

$$6 + 4 = \boxed{}$$

$$3 + 7 = \boxed{}$$

$$8 + 2 = \boxed{}$$

$$5 + 5 = \boxed{}$$

$$1 + 9 = \boxed{}$$

$$4 + 6 = \boxed{}$$

Speedy adding

As quickly as you can, add these numbers in your head. Say the answers aloud, then write them in the boxes.

7 add 2

11 add 11

4 plus 4

9 plus 7

6 and 6

12 + 12

3 add 8

6 and 5

9 plus 4

eight plus two

7 + 7

9 add 8

5 and 5

11 plus 12

10 + 11

4 and 8

8 + 7

one add six

6 plus 8

Farmyard frolics

Answer these addition stories. Write your answers in the boxes.

a. There are **10** sheep. They meet up with **9** more sheep. How many sheep are there altogether?

b. Farmer Stan collects **3** hay bales on Monday, **2** on Tuesday and **3** on Wednesday. How many hay bales does he collect altogether?

c. One cat has **3** kittens, another cat has **4** kittens and another cat has **5** kittens. How many kittens are there altogether?

d. One chicken lays **4** eggs and the other chicken lays **7** eggs. How many eggs are there altogether?

Twenty-twenty vision

Solve these problems by adding the numbers up in your head. Say your answers aloud then write them in the boxes.

3 + 7 = ☐   15 + 5 = ☐

0 + 10 = ☐   2 + 18 = ☐

3 + 12 = ☐   16 + 4 = ☐

14 + 6 = ☐   2 + 18 = ☐

9 + 11 = ☐   17 + 3 = ☐

Brain teasers

As quickly as you can, try answering these problems in your head. Write your answers in the boxes.

a. 1 more than **5** is ☐

b. 2 more than **3** is ☐

c. 4 more than **6** is ☐   **e. 9** more than **3** is ☐

d. 5 more than **5** is ☐   **f. 7** more than **7** is ☐

g. 11 more than **9** is ☐

h. 8 more than **4** is ☐

    i. 3 more than **2** is ☐

j. 10 more than **12** is ☐

k. 4 more than **2** is ☐

l. 9 more than **6** is ☐

Adding in your head

Try adding **three** numbers together in your head. Say your answers aloud then write them in the boxes.

4 + 5 + 3 = ☐

6 + 3 + 2 = ☐

5 + 6 + 7 = ☐

2 + 3 + 4 = ☐

3 + 5 + 7 = ☐

8 + 1 + 9 = ☐

Fishing for 20

Join the numbers on the penguins and fish that together total 20.
The first one has been done for you.

e.g.

Subtracting from 10

Solve these addition problems in your head. Say your answers aloud then write them in the boxes.

10 – 7 = ⬜   10 – 1 = ⬜

10 – 4 = ⬜   10 – 9 = ⬜

10 – 3 = ⬜   10 – 6 = ⬜

10 – 8 = ⬜   10 – 10 = ⬜

10 – 0 = ⬜   10 – 2 = ⬜

Subtracting numbers

As quickly as you can, subtract these numbers in your head. Write your answers in the boxes.

12 minus 5 =

10 take away 2 is

11 take away 7 equals

15 minus 5 =

7 take away 4 is

6 from 9 is

5 from 20 is

3 subtract 2 equals

13 – 5 =

14 – 7 =

20 minus 17 equals

nine minus three equals

4 subtract 2 is

19 from 20 =

74

Pond problems

Answer these subtraction stories. Write your answers in the boxes.

a. There are **12** ducks on the pond, then **6** ducks swim away. How many are left?

b. **14** frogs sit on the lily pads. If **8** frogs hop away, how many remain?

c. There are **18** snails by the pond. **6** snails slide away and **4** more follow them. How many snails remain?

d. If **5** out of **13** birds fly away, how many are left?

Operations in your head

Answer these adding and subtracting problems in your head.
Say the answers aloud then write your answers in the boxes.

5 + 4 - 3 = ☐

2 + 6 - 3 = ☐

4 + 7 - 5 = ☐

8 + 5 - 4 = ☐

9 + 7 - 2 = ☐

4 + 6 + 8 - 7 = ☐

7 + 3 + 8 - 9 = ☐

Number trails

Do these spooky sums and write your answers in the boxes.

2 + 3 + 5 = ☐

2 + 2 + 2 = ☐

6 + 1 + 3 = ☐

4 + 1 + 6 = ☐

7 + 2 + 3 = ☐

0 + 5 + 0 = ☐

4 + 3 + 4 = ☐

1 + 10 + 10 = ☐

9 + 3 + 3 = ☐

10 + 10 + 10 = ☐

What comes next?

Look at the number sequences below. Work out which number comes next and write your answers in the boxes.

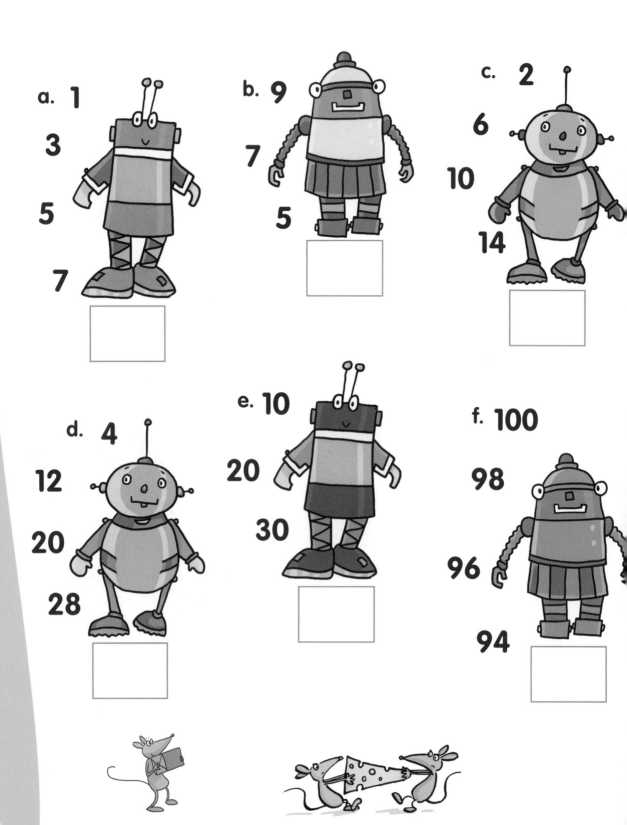

a. 1
3
5
7

b. 9
7
5

c. 2
6
10
14

d. 4
12
20
28

e. 10
20
30

f. 100
98
96
94

Let's get ready to double!

Try doubling these numbers in your head by partitioning the numbers into tens and units. Add them up, then write your answers in the boxes.

e.g. double **14**

tens	units
1	4

10 + 4

double **10** = **20**   double **4** = **8**

20 + **8** = **28**

double **21** = [　　　]   double **13** = [　　　]

double **24** = [　　　]   double **32** = [　　　]

double **35** = [　　　]   double **42** = [　　　]

79

Number bonds to 100

Complete these number bonds by writing the answers in the boxes. **Hint: 2 + 8 = 10** so **20 + 80 = 100**.

$30 + \boxed{} = 100$

$40 + \boxed{} = 100$

$50 + \boxed{} = 100$

$80 + \boxed{} = 100$

$10 + \boxed{} = 100$

Flying high

Join the pairs of numbers that have a difference of 4.

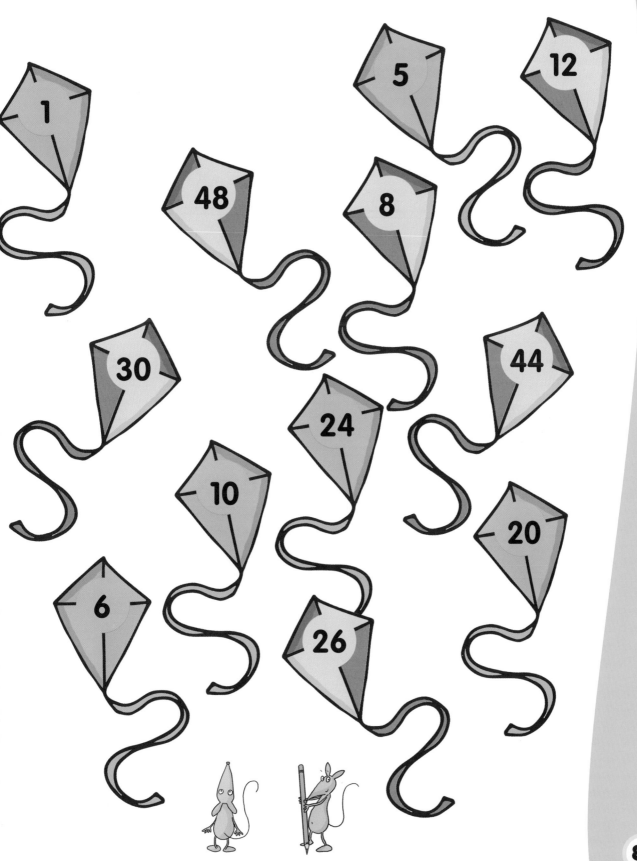

Multiplication madness

Complete these multiplication tables.

1 x 3 =

2 x 3 =

3 x 3 =

4 x 3 =

5 x 3 =

6 x 3 =

7 x 3 =

8 x 3 =

9 x 3 =

10 x 3 =

11 x 3 =

12 x 3 =

1 x 4 =

2 x 4 =

3 x 4 =

4 x 4 =

5 x 4 =

6 x 4 =

7 x 4 =

8 x 4 =

9 x 4 =

10 x 4 =

11 x 4 =

12 x 4 =

1 x 5 =		1 x 10 =	
2 x 5 =		2 x 10 =	
3 x 5 =		3 x 10 =	
4 x 5 =		4 x 10 =	
5 x 5 =		5 x 10 =	
6 x 5 =		6 x 10 =	
7 x 5 =		7 x 10 =	
8 x 5 =		8 x 10 =	
9 x 5 =		9 x 10 =	
10 x 5 =		10 x 10 =	
11 x 5 =		11 x 10 =	
12 x 5 =		12 x 10 =	

The four operations

Below are some subtraction, addition, multiplication and division problems. See how quickly you can do them in your head. Write your answers in the boxes.

65 − 5 = ☐   18 − 5 = ☐

14 + 5 = ☐   17 + 7 = ☐

8 × 8 = ☐   7 × 3 = ☐

9 ÷ 3 = ☐

10 ÷ 2 = ☐

Multiplying by 10

By adding 0 to the end of a number, you multiply it by 10.
Do these multiplications and write your answers in the boxes.

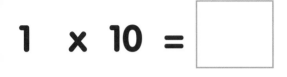

1 x 10 = ☐   2 x 10 = ☐

3 x 10 = ☐   4 x 10 = ☐

5 x 10 = ☐   6 x 10 = ☐

7 x 10 = ☐   10 x 10 = ☐

100 x 10 = ☐   1000 x 10 = ☐

Count with Dracula

Work out the sums in your head as quickly as you can.

3 × 2 =

4 × 9 =

20 ÷ 5 =

12 – 6 =

5 + 4 =

3 × 3 =

7 – 2 =

3 + 7 =

19 – 7 =

1 × 8 =

11 – 6 =

6 ÷ 2 =

7 – 3 =

8 + 2 =

1 × 0 =

3 × 6 =

10 ÷ 1 =

5 × 4 =

18 – 5 =

9 + 2 =

1 + 1 =

Dividing

Using the numbers in the balloons, answer the division problems below.

$6 \div 2 =$ ☐

$10 \div 2 =$ ☐

$14 \div 2 =$ ☐

$60 \div 6 =$ ☐

$88 \div 8 =$ ☐

$5 \div 1 =$ ☐

$12 \div 3 =$ ☐

$12 \div 12 =$ ☐

$20 \div 10 =$ ☐

$6 \div 3 =$ ☐

$24 \div 6 =$ ☐

$14 \div 7 =$ ☐

Dividing by 10

By removing 0 from the end of a number, you divide it by 10. Do these divisions and write your answers in the boxes.

10 ÷ 10 = ☐   20 ÷ 10 = ☐

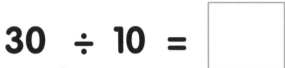

30 ÷ 10 = ☐   40 ÷ 10 = ☐

50 ÷ 10 = ☐   60 ÷ 10 = ☐

70 ÷ 10 = ☐   80 ÷ 10 = ☐

90 ÷ 10 = ☐   100 ÷ 10 = ☐

Double double

Can you double these numbers and then double them again?
Hint: it is the same as multiplying by 4.

e.g. double **8** = $\boxed{16}$ double **16** = $\boxed{32}$

double double **15** = ☐

double double **9** = ☐

double double **100** = ☐

double double **12** = ☐

double double **25** = ☐

double double **7** = ☐

Half the bother

Can you halve these numbers and then halve them again?
Hint: it is the same as dividing by 4.

e.g. half **32** = ☐ 16 ☐   half **16** = ☐ 8 ☐

half half **16** = ☐

half half **12** = ☐

half half **40** = ☐

half half **48** = ☐

half half **8** = ☐

half half **100** = ☐

Shapes

Answer these questions about shapes.

a. How many sides does
a square have?

 sides

b. How many sides do
4 squares have altogether?

 sides

c. How many faces does
a cube have?

 faces

d. How many sides does
a triangle have?

 sides

e. How many sides do
7 triangles have altogether?

 sides

. How many flat faces
does a cylinder have?

 faces

Speed test 1

Answer these questions as quickly as you can.
Write your answers in the boxes.

a. **7** add **13** is

b. What is **6** more than **12?**

c. **12** x **12** =

d. How many sides do **5** squares have altogether?

e. **5** eggs add **5** eggs take away **3** eggs equals

f. **2** + **14** + **6** =

g. **9** buns divided between **3** elephants =

Speed test 2

Answer these questions as quickly as you can.
Write your answers in the boxes.

a. **100 ÷ 10 =**

b. add **20** to **15 =**

c. **12** take away **7 =**

d. **3 + 5 + 15 =**

e. **13 + 4 + 4 =**

f. There are **18** mice. The cat chases
   6 mice. How many are left?

g. Triangles have **6** sides altogether.
   True or false?

Speed test 3

Answer these questions as quickly as you can.
Write your answers in the boxes.

a. 7 birds from **13** birds equals

b. **3**

6

9

12

c. 90

70

50

30

d. **25**

20

15

10

e. 3 × 3 × 3 =

f. 16 from **20** equals

g. 4 + 7 + 2 + 1 =

Answers

Get ready!

6 + 4 = **10**	3 + 7 = **10**
8 + 2 = **10**	5 + 5 = **10**
1 + 9 = **10**	4 + 6 = **10**

Speedy adding

7 + 2 = **9**	11 + 11 = **22**
4 + 4 = **8**	9 + 7 = **16**
6 + 6 = **12**	12 + 12 = **24**
3 + 8 = **11**	6 + 5 = **11**
9 + 4 = **13**	8 + 2 = **10**
7 + 7 = **14**	9 + 8 = **17**
5 + 5 = **10**	11 + 12 = **23**
10 + 11 = **21**	4 + 8 = **12**
8 + 7 = **15**	1 + 6 = **7**
6 + 8 = **14**	

Farmyard frolics

a. 19 b. 8 c. 12 d. 11

Twenty-twenty vision

13 + 7 = **20**	15 + 5 = **20**
10 + 10 = **20**	2 + 18 = **20**
8 + 12 = **20**	16 + 4 = **20**
14 + 6 = **20**	2 + 18 = **20**
9 + 11 = **20**	17 + 3 = **20**

Brain teasers

a. 6   b. 5   c. 10   d. 10
e. 12   f. 14   g. 20   h. 12
i. 5   j. 22   k. 6   l. 15

Adding in your head

4 + 5 + 3 = **12**
6 + 3 + 2 = **11**
5 + 6 + 7 = **18**
2 + 3 + 4 = **9**
3 + 5 + 7 = **15**
8 + 1 + 9 = **18**

Fishing for 20

15 – 5	2 – 18
16 – 4	6 – 14
19 – 1	7 – 13
10 – 10	9 – 11

Subtracting from 10

10 – 7 = **3**	10 – 1 = **9**
10 – 4 = **6**	10 – 9 = **1**
10 – 3 = **7**	10 – 6 = **4**
10 – 8 = **2**	10 – 10 = **0**
10 – 0 = **10**	10 – 2 = **8**

Subtracting numbers

12 – 5 = **7**	10 – 2 = **8**
11 – 7 = **4**	15 – 5 = **10**
7 – 4 = **3**	9 – 6 = **3**
20 – 5 = **15**	3 – 2 = **1**
13 – 5 = **8**	14 – 7 = **7**
20 – 17 = **3**	9 – 3 = **6**
4 – 2 = **2**	20 – 19 = **1**

Pond problems

a. 12 – 6 = **6**   b. 14 – 8 = **6**
c. 18 – 6 – 4 = **8**   d. 13 – 5 = **8**

Operations in your head

5 + 4 – 3 = **6**
2 + 6 – 3 = **5**
4 + 7 – 5 = **6**
8 + 5 – 4 = **9**
9 + 7 – 2 = **14**
4 + 6 + 8 – 7 = **11**
7 + 3 + 8 – 9 = **9**

Number trails

2 + 3 + 5 = **10**
2 + 2 + 2 = **6**
6 + 1 + 3 = **10**
4 + 1 + 6 = **11**
7 + 2 + 3 = **12**
0 + 5 + 0 = **5**
4 + 3 + 4 = **11**
1 + 10 + 10 = **21**
9 + 3 + 3 = **15**
10 + 10 + 10 = **30**

What comes next?

a. 9 b. 3 c. 18 d. 36 e. 40 f. 92

Let's get ready to double!

double 21 = **42**	double 13 = **26**
double 24 = **48**	double 32 = **64**
double 35 = **70**	double 42 = **84**

Number bonds to 100

30 + **70** = 100	40 + **60** = 100
50 + **50** = 100	80 + **20** = 100
10 + **90** = 100	

Flying high

5 – 1	48 – 44
12 – 8	30 – 26
10 – 6	24 – 20

Answers

Multiplication madness

1 x 3 = **3**	1 x 4 = **4**
2 x 3 = **6**	2 x 4 = **8**
3 x 3 = **9**	3 x 4 = **12**
4 x 3 = **12**	4 x 4 = **16**
5 x 3 = **15**	5 x 4 = **20**
6 x 3 = **18**	6 x 4 = **24**
7 x 3 = **21**	7 x 4 = **28**
8 x 3 = **24**	8 x 4 = **32**
9 x 3 = **27**	9 x 4 = **36**
10 x 3 = **30**	10 x 4 = **40**
11 x 3 = **33**	11 x 4 = **44**
12 x 3 = **36**	12 x 4 = **48**

1 x 5 = **5**	1 x 10 = **10**
2 x 5 = **10**	2 x 10 = **20**
3 x 5 = **15**	3 x 10 = **30**
4 x 5 = **20**	4 x 10 = **40**
5 x 5 = **25**	5 x 10 = **50**
6 x 5 = **30**	6 x 10 = **60**
7 x 5 = **35**	7 x 10 = **70**
8 x 5 = **40**	8 x 10 = **80**
9 x 5 = **45**	9 x 10 = **90**
10 x 5 = **50**	10 x 10 = **100**
11 x 5 = **55**	11 x 10 = **110**
12 x 5 = **60**	12 x 10 = **120**

The four operations

65 – 5 = **60**	18 – 5 = **13**
14 + 5 = **19**	17 + 7 = **24**
8 x 8 = **64**	7 x 3 = **21**
9 ÷ 3 = **3**	
10 ÷ 2 = **5**	

Multiplying by 10

1 x 10 = **10**	2 x 10 = **20**
3 x 10 = **30**	4 x 10 = **40**
5 x 10 = **50**	6 x 10 = **60**
7 x 10 = **70**	10 x 10 = **100**
100 x 10 = **1,000**	1000 x 10 = **10,000**

Count with Dracula

3 x 2 = **6**	3 + 7 = **10**
4 x 9 = **36**	19 – 7 = **12**
20 ÷ 5 = **4**	1 x 8 = **8**
12 – 6 = **6**	11 – 6 = **5**
5 + 4 = **9**	6 ÷ 2 = **3**
3 x 3 = **9**	7 – 3 = **4**
7 – 2 = **5**	8 + 2 = **10**
1 x 0 = **0**	
3 x 6 = **18**	
10 ÷ 1 = **10**	
5 x 4 = **20**	
18 – 5 = **13**	
9 + 2 = **11**	
1 + 1 = **2**	

Dividing

6 ÷ 2 = **3**	10 ÷ 2 = **5**
14 ÷ 2 = **7**	60 ÷ 6 = **10**
88 ÷ 8 = **11**	5 ÷ 1 = **5**
12 ÷ 3 = **4**	12 ÷ 12 = **1**
20 ÷ 10 = **2**	6 ÷ 3 = **2**
24 ÷ 6 = **4**	14 ÷ 7 = **2**

Dividing by 10

10 ÷ 10 = **1**	20 ÷ 10 = **2**
30 ÷ 10 = **3**	40 ÷ 10 = **4**
50 ÷ 10 = **5**	60 ÷ 10 = **6**
70 ÷ 10 = **7**	80 ÷ 10 = **8**
90 ÷ 10 = **9**	100 ÷ 10 = **10**

Double double

double double 15 = **60**
double double 9 = **36**
double double 100 = **400**
double double 12 = **48**
double double 25 = **100**
double double 7 = **28**

Half the bother

half half 16 = **4**
half half 12 = **3**
half half 40 = **10**
half half 48 = **12**
half half 8 = **2**
half half 100 = **25**

Shapes

a. **4** sides b. **16** sides c. **6** faces
d. **3** sides e. **21** sides f. **2** faces

Speed test 1

a. 7 add 13 is **20**
b. 6 more than 12 is **18**
c. 12 x 12 = **144**
d. **20 sides**
e. **7 eggs**
f. 2 + 14 + 6 = **22**
g. **3 buns**

Speed test 2

a. 100 ÷ 10 = **10**
b. add 20 to 15 = **35**
c. 12 take away 7 = **5**
d. 3 + 5 + 15 = **23**
e. 13 + 4 + 4 = **21**
f. **12 mice**
g. **false**

Speed test 3

a. **6 birds**
b. **15** c. **10** d. **5**
e. 3 x 3 x 3 = **27**
f. 16 from 20 = **4**
g. 4 + 7 + 2 + 1 = **14**

Times Tables

In Year Two (age 7+) your child is expected to be able to:

• Recall and use multiplication facts for the 2, 5 and 10 times tables, including recognising odd and even numbers.

• Calculate the answers to multiplication statements using multiplication (x) and equals (=) signs.

• Solve multiplication problems using materials, array, repeated addition, mental methods and multiplication and division facts, including problems in context.

Glossary

Materials: Physical objects used to aid learning, for example, having 10 pencils and sharing them between 2 to find the answer to 10 ÷ 2.

Array: Using dots to represent numbers, for example 4 x 5 would be represented by 4 rows of dots, each row 5 dots in length.

Repeated addition: To answer 5 x 4 you could add 5, four times: 5 + 5 + 5 + 5 = 20.

Problems in context: Mathematical problems expressed as text, for example, Sam has 5 friends and wants to give them each 2 biscuits. How many biscuits does Sam need? This can be expressed simply as a multiplication problem: 5 x 2 = 10.

1 and 2 times tables

Complete these multiplication tables.

1 x 1 =		1 x 2 =	
2 x 1 =		2 x 2 =	
3 x 1 =		3 x 2 =	
4 x 1 =		4 x 2 =	
5 x 1 =		5 x 2 =	
6 x 1 =		6 x 2 =	
7 x 1 =		7 x 2 =	
8 x 1 =		8 x 2 =	
9 x 1 =		9 x 2 =	
10 x 1 =		10 x 2 =	
11 x 1 =		11 x 2 =	
12 x 1 =		12 x 2 =	

3 and 4 times tables

Complete these multiplication tables.

1 x 3 =   1 x 4 =

2 x 3 =   2 x 4 =

3 x 3 =   3 x 4 =

4 x 3 =   4 x 4 =

5 x 3 =   5 x 4 =

6 x 3 =   6 x 4 =

7 x 3 =   7 x 4 =

8 x 3 =   8 x 4 =

9 x 3 =   9 x 4 =

10 x 3 =   10 x 4 =

11 x 3 =   11 x 4 =

12 x 3 =   12 x 4 =

5 and 6 times tables

Complete these multiplication tables.

1 x 5 = ☐   1 x 6 = ☐

2 x 5 = ☐   2 x 6 = ☐

3 x 5 = ☐   3 x 6 = ☐

4 x 5 = ☐   4 x 6 = ☐

5 x 5 = ☐   5 x 6 = ☐

6 x 5 = ☐   6 x 6 = ☐

7 x 5 = ☐   7 x 6 = ☐

8 x 5 = ☐   8 x 6 = ☐

9 x 5 = ☐   9 x 6 = ☐

10 x 5 = ☐   10 x 6 = ☐

11 x 5 = ☐   11 x 6 = ☐

12 x 5 = ☐   12 x 6 = ☐

7 and 8 times tables

Complete these multiplication tables.

1 × 7 = ⬜   1 × 8 = ⬜

2 × 7 = ⬜   2 × 8 = ⬜

3 × 7 = ⬜   3 × 8 = ⬜

4 × 7 = ⬜   4 × 8 = ⬜

5 × 7 = ⬜   5 × 8 = ⬜

6 × 7 = ⬜   6 × 8 = ⬜

7 × 7 = ⬜   7 × 8 = ⬜

8 × 7 = ⬜   8 × 8 = ⬜

9 × 7 = ⬜   9 × 8 = ⬜

10 × 7 = ⬜   10 × 8 = ⬜

11 × 7 = ⬜   11 × 8 = ⬜

12 × 7 = ⬜   12 × 8 = ⬜

9 and 10 times tables

Complete these multiplication tables.

1 x 9 = ☐   1 x 10 = ☐

2 x 9 = ☐   2 x 10 = ☐

3 x 9 = ☐   3 x 10 = ☐

4 x 9 = ☐   4 x 10 = ☐

5 x 9 = ☐   5 x 10 = ☐

6 x 9 = ☐   6 x 10 = ☐

7 x 9 = ☐   7 x 10 = ☐

8 x 9 = ☐   8 x 10 = ☐

9 x 9 = ☐   9 x 10 = ☐

10 x 9 = ☐   10 x 10 = ☐

11 x 9 = ☐   11 x 10 = ☐

12 x 9 = ☐   12 x 10 = ☐

11 and 12 times tables

Complete these multiplication tables.

1 x 11 = ☐   1 x 12 = ☐

2 x 11 = ☐   2 x 12 = ☐

3 x 11 = ☐   3 x 12 = ☐

4 x 11 = ☐   4 x 12 = ☐

5 x 11 = ☐   5 x 12 = ☐

6 x 11 = ☐   6 x 12 = ☐

7 x 11 = ☐   7 x 12 = ☐

8 x 11 = ☐   8 x 12 = ☐

9 x 11 = ☐   9 x 12 = ☐

10 x 11 = ☐   10 x 12 = ☐

11 x 11 = ☐   11 x 12 = ☐

12 x 11 = ☐   12 x 10 = ☐

Picture problems

Work out the multiplications and write the answers in the boxes. Use your completed times tables to help you.

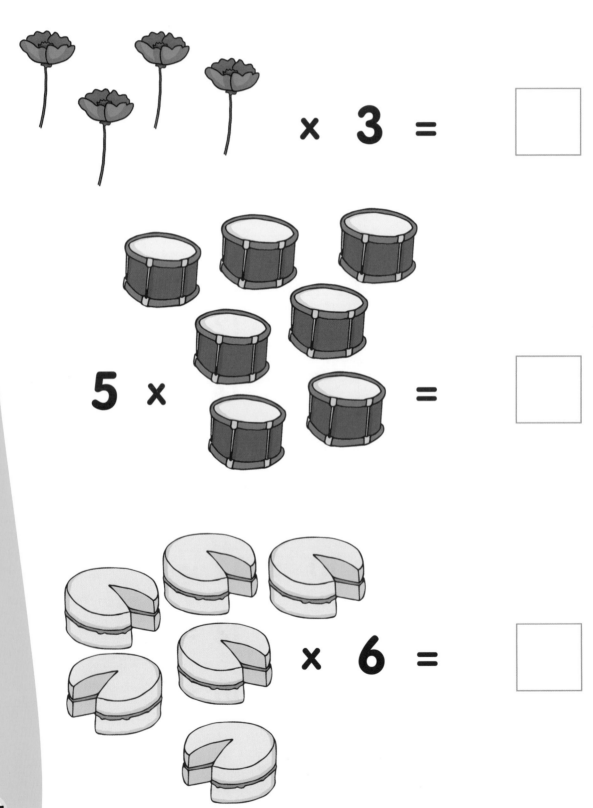

$\times\ 3 =$ ☐

$5\ \times$ $=$ ☐

$\times\ 6 =$ ☐

Creepy crawly problems

Write the missing numbers in the boxes to complete the multiplications.

     × **3** =

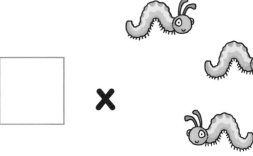 × =

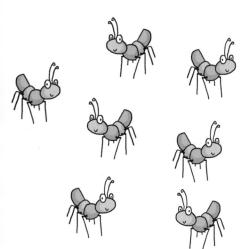 × **4** =

Metal multiplication

Complete these robot multiplications by writing the missing numbers in the boxes.

Multiplication puzzles

Write the missing numbers to complete the puzzles.

	×	3	=	9
×	■	×	■	×
1	×	2	=	
=	■	=	■	=
3	×		=	18

5	×		=	10
×	■	×	■	×
	×		=	5
=	■	=	■	=
5	×	10	=	

Snakes and ladders

Work out the multiplications and write the answers in the snakes and ladders puzzle.

10 × 4 = _____

11
×
8
=
_____

8
×
8
=
_____

8 × 7 = _____

Galaxy gazing

Do the multiplications to join the aliens with their planets.

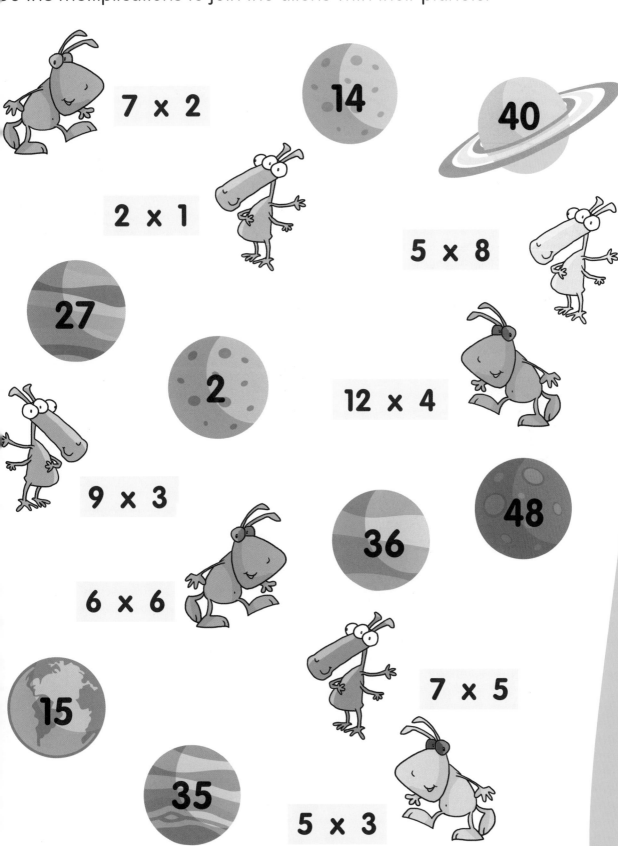

7 x 2

14

40

2 x 1

5 x 8

27

2

12 x 4

9 x 3

48

36

6 x 6

15

7 x 5

35

5 x 3

Shooting stars

Do the multiplications to join the fairies with their shooting stars.

20 0 4

45 16

21 48

9

2 x 2   8 x 0   10 x 2

6 x 8   3 x 7   5 x 9

4 x 4   3 x 3

Multiplication puzzles

Write the missing numbers to complete the puzzles.

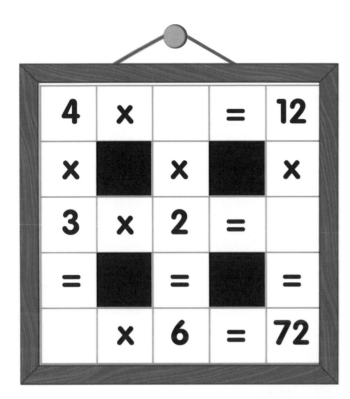

4	×		=	12
×	■	×	■	×
3	×	2	=	
=	■	=	■	=
	×	6	=	72

	×	2	=	12
×	■	×	■	×
1	×		=	3
=	■	=	■	=
	×	6	=	36

Multiplication test 1

Complete the multiplications by writing the missing numbers in the boxes. Then, write the missing number word on the line next to the sum.

9 × ☐ = 81 _____

☐ × 7 = 56 _____

6 × 10 = ☐ _____

4 × 5 = ☐ _____

☐ × 9 = 36 _____

☐ × 1 = 11 _____

7 × 2 = ☐ _____

1 × 5 = ☐ _____

Painting problems

Work out the answers to the multiplications on the ladders.
Write the answers on the buckets.

9 × 9 =

6 × 12 =

5 × 6 =

Multiplication crossword

Do the multiplications and write the answers in the boxes. Then write the answers as words in the crossword grid.

1. → 8 × 2 = ☐

1. ↓ 17 × 1 = ☐

2. 3 × 3 = ☐

3. → 1 × 2 = ☐

3. ↓ 4 × 3 = ☐

4. 2 × 4 = ☐

5. 11 × 1 = ☐

6. 1 × 1 = ☐

7. 10 × 8 = ☐

8. 9 × 1 = ☐

Puzzling problems

Help Wanda Witch solve these puzzling problems.
Write the answers in the boxes.

If **1** bag of slime makes **3** cups of smelly
potion, how many cups of potion can
Wanda make with **3** bags of slime?

If Wanda makes **3** test tubes of smelly
potion in **1** hour, how many tubes can
she make in **4** hours?

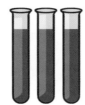

If **5** wizards each buy **5** of Wanda's recipes,
how many recipes will she sell altogether?

Multiplication test 2

Complete the multiplications by writing the missing numbers in the boxes. Then, write the missing number word on the line next to the sum.

12 × 1 = [ ] _____

5 × 4 = [ ] _____

7 × 2 = [ ] _____

4 × 4 = [ ] _____

8 × 1 = [ ] _____

3 × 3 = [ ] _____

11 × 1 = [ ] _____

1 × 1 = [ ] _____

Computer crazy

Tick the correct answers and cross the incorrect answers.

6 X 1 = 6	☐	11 X 11 = 121	☐
7 X 6 = 42	☐	9 X 2 = 18	☐
9 X 9 = 108	☐	5 X 0 = 5	☐
2 X 5 = 10	☐	12 X 2 = 48	☐
3 X 7 = 31	☐	12 X 12 = 4	☐
5 X 9 = 55	☐	0 X 9 = 0	☐
6 X 11 = 66	☐	10 X 2 = 20	☐
10 X 10 = 99	☐	3 X 8 = 24	☐

117

Multiplication crossword

Do the multiplications and write the answers in the boxes. Then write the answers as words in the crossword grid.

1. 10 × 7 = ☐

2. 9 × 2 = ☐

3. 1 × 13 = ☐

4. 5 × 0 = ☐

5. 1 × 1 = ☐

6. 1 × 2 = ☐

7. 4 × 3 = ☐

8. 11 × 1 = ☐

9. 4 × 2 = ☐

10. 10 × 9 = ☐

Right or wrong?

Tick the correct answers and cross the incorrect answers.

6 x 4 = 24 ☐   9 x 6 = 34 ☐

5 x 5 = 35 ☐   9 x 9 = 81 ☐

7 x 2 = 14 ☐   7 x 7 = 49 ☐

8 x 9 = 64 ☐   12 x 10 = 120 ☐

6 x 2 = 12 ☐   5 x 8 = 45 ☐

4 x 3 = 12 ☐   3 x 3 = 9 ☐

7 x 3 = 21 ☐   5 x 10 = 50 ☐

12 x 4 = 28 ☐   8 x 3 = 34 ☐

10 x 3 = 3 ☐   5 x 11 = 55 ☐

Multiplication puzzles

Write the missing numbers to complete the puzzles.

3	×		=	9
×	■	×	■	×
	×	2	=	8
=	■	=	■	=
12	×		=	72

	×	5	=	5
×	■	×	■	×
4	×		=	
=	■	=	■	=
4	×	10	=	40

Multiplication crossword

Do the multiplications and write the answers in the boxes. Then write the answers as words in the crossword grid.

1. 6 × 3 =

2. 6 × 2 =

3.→ 10 × 10 =

3.↓ 1 × 1 =

4. 4 × 2 =

5.→ 1 × 5 =

5.↓ 7 × 2 =

6. 7 × 10 =

7.→ 5 × 2 =

7.↓ 5 × 4 =

Problem solving

Help Arthur the astronaut solve these solar problems.
Write the answers in the boxes.

If **6** astronauts can fit in **1** rocket, how
many astronauts can fit in **3** rockets?

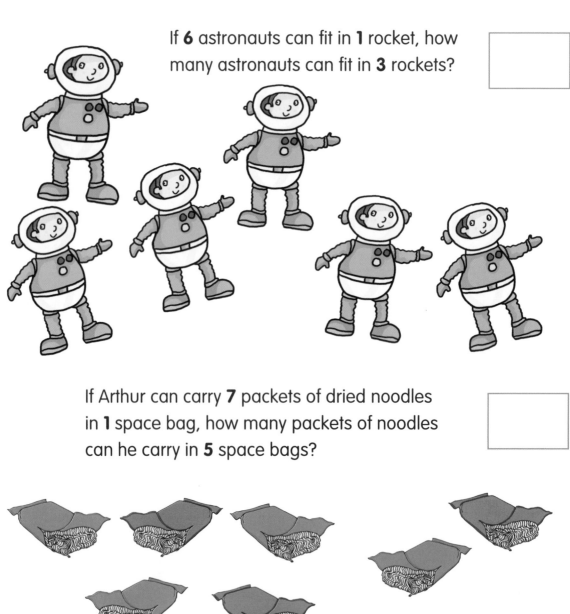

If Arthur can carry **7** packets of dried noodles
in **1** space bag, how many packets of noodles
can he carry in **5** space bags?

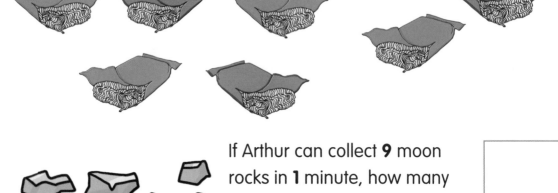

If Arthur can collect **9** moon
rocks in **1** minute, how many
can he collect in **3** minutes?

Jungle Jim

Jungle Jim wants to get back to his tree house. Help him swing through the jungle by colouring the three vines whose numbers are in the 6, 8 and 9 times tables.

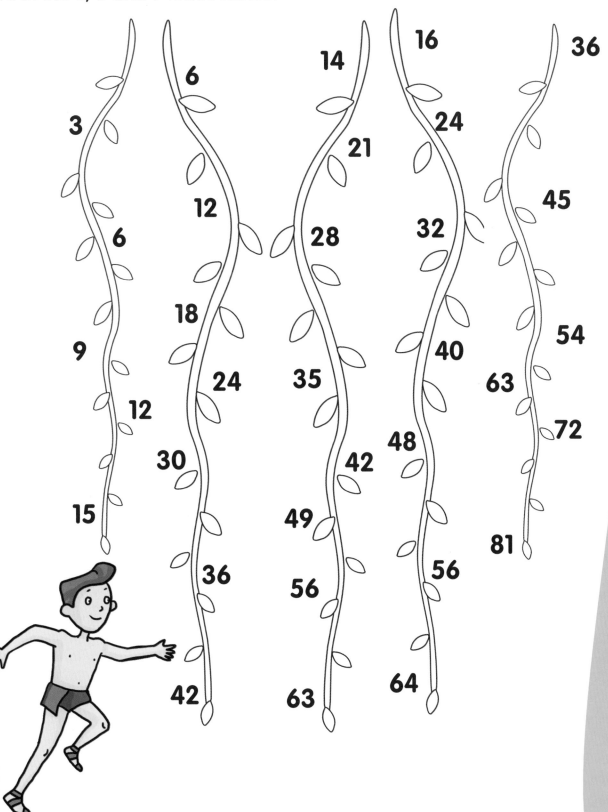

Multiplication test 3

Complete the multiplications by writing the missing numbers in the boxes. Then, write the missing number word on the line next to the sum.

8 × 2 = ☐ _____

☐ × 4 = 12 _____

6 × ☐ = 36 _____

3 × ☐ = 27 _____

12 × ☐ = 144 _____

3 × 5 = ☐ _____

☐ × 2 = 18 _____

10 × 5 = ☐ _____

Test time 1

Do these multiplications. Write the answers in the boxes.

2 × 4 =

5 × 8 =

5 × 7 =

2 × 5 =

6 × 6 =

10 × 5 =

12 × 4 =

6 × 8 =

7 × 0 =

11 × 10 =

8 × 12 =

6 × 9 =

9 × 8 =

1 × 1 =

2 × 2 =

12 × 11 =

1 × 7 =

5 × 2 =

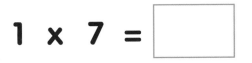

11 × 6 =

8 × 8 =

5 × 9 =

9 × 4 =

9 × 2 =

6 × 3 =

Test time 2

Complete these multiplications by writing the answers in the boxes.

3 × 0 = ☐   8 × ☐ = 64

4 × 4 = ☐   10 × 3 = ☐

9 × ☐ = 18   5 × 9 = ☐

☐ × 8 = 24   11 × 9 = ☐

☐ × 7 = 49   9 × 8 = ☐

6 × ☐ = 12   ☐ × 3 = 24

4 × ☐ = 32   6 × 1 = ☐

☐ × 9 = 81   ☐ × 3 = 30

12 × 6 = ☐   2 × ☐ = 14

10 × ☐ = 70   7 × 7 = ☐

☐ × 7 = 77   9 × ☐ = 27

Answers

1 and 2 times tables

1	x	1	=	1	1	x	2	=	2
2	x	1	=	2	2	x	2	=	4
3	x	1	=	3	3	x	2	=	6
4	x	1	=	4	4	x	2	=	8
5	x	1	=	5	5	x	2	=	10
6	x	1	=	6	6	x	2	=	12
7	x	1	=	7	7	x	2	=	14
8	x	1	=	8	8	x	2	=	16
9	x	1	=	9	9	x	2	=	18
10	x	1	=	10	10	x	2	=	20
11	x	1	=	11	11	x	2	=	22
12	x	1	=	12	12	x	2	=	24

3 and 4 times tables

1	x	3	=	3	1	x	4	=	4
2	x	3	=	6	2	x	4	=	8
3	x	3	=	9	3	x	4	=	12
4	x	3	=	12	4	x	4	=	16
5	x	3	=	15	5	x	4	=	20
6	x	3	=	18	6	x	4	=	24
7	x	3	=	21	7	x	4	=	28
8	x	3	=	24	8	x	4	=	32
9	x	3	=	27	9	x	4	=	36
10	x	3	=	30	10	x	4	=	40
11	x	3	=	33	11	x	4	=	44
12	x	3	=	36	12	x	4	=	48

5 and 6 times tables

1	x	5	=	5	1	x	6	=	6
2	x	5	=	10	2	x	6	=	12
3	x	5	=	15	3	x	6	=	18
4	x	5	=	20	4	x	6	=	24
5	x	5	=	25	5	x	6	=	30
6	x	5	=	30	6	x	6	=	36
7	x	5	=	35	7	x	6	=	42
8	x	5	=	40	8	x	6	=	48
9	x	5	=	45	9	x	6	=	54
10	x	5	=	50	10	x	6	=	60
11	x	5	=	55	11	x	6	=	66
12	x	5	=	60	12	x	6	=	72

7 and 8 times tables

1	x	7	=	7	1	x	8	=	8
2	x	7	=	14	2	x	8	=	16
3	x	7	=	21	3	x	8	=	24
4	x	7	=	28	4	x	8	=	32
5	x	7	=	35	5	x	8	=	40
6	x	7	=	42	6	x	8	=	48
7	x	7	=	49	7	x	8	=	56
8	x	7	=	56	8	x	8	=	64
9	x	7	=	63	9	x	8	=	72
10	x	7	=	70	10	x	8	=	80
11	x	7	=	77	11	x	8	=	88
12	x	7	=	84	12	x	8	=	96

9 and 10 times tables

1	x	9	=	9	1	x	10	=	10
2	x	9	=	18	2	x	10	=	20
3	x	9	=	27	3	x	10	=	30
4	x	9	=	36	4	x	10	=	40
5	x	9	=	45	5	x	10	=	50
6	x	9	=	54	6	x	10	=	60
7	x	9	=	63	7	x	10	=	70
8	x	9	=	72	8	x	10	=	80
9	x	9	=	81	9	x	10	=	90
10	x	9	=	90	10	x	10	=	100
11	x	9	=	99	11	x	10	=	110
12	x	9	=	108	12	x	10	=	120

11 and 12 times tables

1	x	11	=	11	1	x	12	=	12
2	x	11	=	22	2	x	12	=	24
3	x	11	=	33	3	x	12	=	36
4	x	11	=	44	4	x	12	=	48
5	x	11	=	55	5	x	12	=	60
6	x	11	=	66	6	x	12	=	72
7	x	11	=	77	7	x	12	=	84
8	x	11	=	88	8	x	12	=	96
9	x	11	=	99	9	x	12	=	108
10	x	11	=	110	10	x	12	=	120
11	x	11	=	121	11	x	12	=	132
12	x	11	=	132	12	x	12	=	144

Picture problems

$4 \times 3 = 12$ $5 \times 7 = 35$
$6 \times 6 = 36$

Creepy crawly problems

$5 \times 3 = 15$ $2 \times 3 = 6$
$7 \times 4 = 28$

Metal multiplication

$6 \times 6 = 36$ $9 \times 5 = 45$
$10 \times 6 = 60$

Multiplication puzzles

3	x	3	=	9
x		x		x
1	x	2	=	2
=		=		=
3	x	6	=	18

5	x	2	=	10
x		x		x
1	x	5	=	5
=		=		=
5	x	10	=	50

Snakes and ladders

$10 \times 4 = 40$ $11 \times 8 = 88$
$8 \times 8 = 64$ $8 \times 7 = 56$

Galaxy gazing

$7 \times 2 = 14$ $9 \times 3 = 27$
$2 \times 1 = 2$ $6 \times 6 = 36$
$5 \times 8 = 40$ $7 \times 5 = 35$
$12 \times 4 = 48$ $5 \times 3 = 15$

Shooting stars

$2 \times 2 = 4$ $3 \times 7 = 21$
$8 \times 0 = 0$ $4 \times 4 = 16$
$10 \times 2 = 20$ $3 \times 3 = 9$
$6 \times 8 = 48$ $5 \times 9 = 45$

Answers

Multiplication puzzles

4	x	3	=	12
x		x		x
3	x	2	=	6
=		=		=
12	x	6	=	72

6	x	2	=	12
x		x		x
1	x	3	=	3
=		=		=
6	x	6	=	36

Multiplication test 1

9 x **9** = 81   nine
8 x 7= 56   eight
6 x 10= **60**   sixty
4 x 5= **20**   twenty
4 x 9= 36   four
11 x 1= 11   eleven
7 x 2= **14**   fourteen
1 x 5= **5**   five

Painting problems

9 x 9 = **81**   6 x 12 = **72**
5 x 6 = **30**

Multiplication crossword

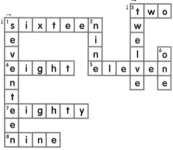

Puzzling problems

9 cups of potion
12 test tubes
25 recipes

Multiplication test 2

12 x 1 = **12**   twelve
5 x 4 =**20**   twenty
7 x 2 =**14**   fourteen
4 x 4 =**16**   sixteen
8 x 1 = **8**   eight
3 x 3 = **9**   nine
11 x 1 = **11**   eleven
1 x 1 = **1**   one

Computer crazy

6 x 1 = 6 ✔
7 x 6 = 42 ✔
9 x 9 = 108 ✘ **(81)**
2 x 5 = 10 ✔
3 x 7 = 31 ✘ **(21)**
5 x 9 = 55 ✘ **(45)**
6 x 11 = 66 ✔
10 x 10 = 99 ✘ **(100)**

11 x 11 = 121 ✔
9 x 2 = 18 ✔
5 x 0 = 5 ✘ **(0)**
12 x 2 = 48 ✘ **(24)**
12 x 12 = 4 ✘ **(144)**
0 x 9 = 0 ✔
10 x 2 = 20 ✔
3 x 8 = 24 ✔

Multiplication crossword

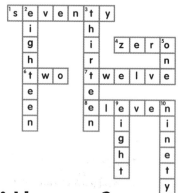

Right or wrong?

6 x 4 = 24 ✔   9 x 6 = 34 ✘ **(54)**
5 x 5 = 35 ✘ **(25)**   9 x 9 = 81 ✔
7 x 2 = 14 ✔   7 x 7 = 49 ✔
8 x 9 = 64 ✘ **(72)**   12 x 10 =120 ✔
6 x 2 = 12 ✔   5 x 8 = 45 ✘ **(40)**
4 x 3 = 12 ✔   3 x 3 = 9 ✔
7 x 3 = 21 ✔   5 x 10 = 50 ✔
12 x 4 = 28 ✘ **(48)**   8 x 3 = 34 ✘ **(24)**
10 x 3 = 3 ✘ **(30)**   5 x 11 = 55 ✔

Multiplication puzzles

3	x	3	=	9
x		x		x
4	x	2	=	8
=		=		=
12	x	6	=	72

1	x	5	=	5
x		x		x
4	x	2	=	8
=		=		=
4	x	10	=	40

Multiplication crossword

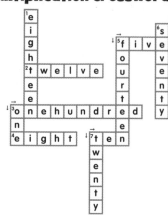

Problem solving

18 astronauts   **35** packets
27 rocks

Jungle Jim

6 12 18 24 30 36 42
16 24 32 40 48 56 64
36 45 54 63 72 81

Multiplication test 3

8 x 2 = **16**   sixteen
3 x 4 =12   three
6 x **6** =36   six
3 x **9** =27   nine
12 x **12** =144   twelve
3 x 5 = **15**   fifteen
9 x 2 = 18   nine
10 x 5 =**50**   fifty

Test time 1

2 x 4 = **8**   5 x 8 = 4
5 x 7 = **35**   2 x 5 = 1
6 x 6 = **36**   10 x 5 = 5
12 x 4 = **48**   6 x 8 = 4
7 x 0 = **0**   11 x 10 = 11
8 x 12 = **96**   6 x 9 = 5
9 x 8 = **72**   1 x 1 =
2 x 2 = **4**   12 x 11 =13
1 x 7 = **7**   5 x 2 = 1
11 x 6 = **66**   8 x 8 = 6
5 x 9 = **45**   9 x 4 = 3
9 x 2 = **18**   6 x 3 = 1

Test time 2

3 x 0 = **0**   8 x **8** = 6
4 x 4 = **16**   10 x 3 = 3
9 x **2** = 18   5 x 9 = 4
3 x 8 = 24   11 x 9 = 9
7 x 7 = 49   9 x 8 = 7
6 x **2** = 12   **8** x 3 = 2
4 x **8** = 32   6 x 1 =
9 x 9 = 81   **10** x 3 = 3
12 x 6 = **72**   2 x **7** = 1
10 x **7** = 70   7 x 7 = 4
11 x 7 = **77**   9 x **3** = 2